C000229254

C. Baerman

COMPLETE METHOD
FOR
CLARINET

Op.63

Edited by
Gustave Langenus

CARL FISCHER®

ISBN 978-0-8258-0170-9

FOREWORD

CARL BAERMANN, the author of this Clarinet Method, was born in Munich in 1820, and died in the same city in 1885. Heinrich Baermann, 1788-1874, father of Carl, was the greatest clarinet player of his day. His name was as well-known in the musical circles of Paris and London as in Munich. He traveled extensively throughout Europe, evoking the greatest enthusiasm wherever he appeared. While in London he was invited by the Prince-Regent, afterwards George IV, to become his guest at the palace during his stay. He was also the protege of Louis Ferdinand, of Prussia, at whose court he often appeared as soloist.

It is recorded that Carl Baermann was even a greater clarinetist than his father. At the age of fourteen he became a member of the Munich Court Band, and after the death of his father was chosen as first clarinet in that organization. When eighteen he was introduced to the European music world by his father in an extended tour throughout the continent. So great were his artistic achievements that King Ludwig of Bavaria showed his appreciation by conferring upon him the gold medal of Arts and Sciences. The Baermanns were intimately acquainted with Carl Maria von Weber, who spoke of Heinrich as "a truly great artist and a glorious man." Weber dedicated most of his clarinet works to Heinrich and was also the godfather of Carl. Mendelssohn wrote some of his most noteworthy letters to Heinrich, two of which are included in the "Letters of Distinguished Musicians."

While Carl Baermann was a wonderful performer on the clarinet, the interest of clarinetists centers particularly on the excellent clarinet method which he composed between the years 1855 and 1865. This work contains a wealth of instructive and melodic material so stimulating as to make one forget it was written for teaching purposes. Baermann was an untiring worker, and in addition to his numerous compositions, was also engaged for many years in endeavoring to improve the mechanical parts of his instrument. The result of these years of labor in this direction was the Baermann System Clarinet. The basis of this system was the same as Muller's thirteen keyed clarinet, to which Baermann added some duplicate fingerings, such as an extra key for the Bb-F taken with the little finger of the left hand, a forked F-C with the left hand, a F sharp — C sharp key operated with the right hand thumb. Theobald Bohm's system of fingering was also utilized by Baermann to some extent.

All the fingerings marked in the original edition of the Baermann Method are, as a matter of course based upon this system. But since the days of Baermann no end of superior improvements have been made in the mechanism of clarinets, and while there may be a few scattered players who still use the "Baermann System," it has become practically obsolete in France, Belgium, Italy and the United States.

While Baermann's "System" has disappeared, his "Clarinet Method" remains as one of the finest works of its kind ever written, and the present new edition has been revised with the special object of modernising it and making it thoroughly acceptable for the practical needs of all present-day players.

In consequence all finger marks referring to the Baermann Clarinet System, which were the cause of so much confusion to modern clarinetists, have been eliminated; the introductory chapter containing Baermann's lengthy description of his invention has been omitted and the form of the first chapter proper has been re-arranged in such a way as to enable the student to follow certain events in their chronological order.

With the exception of these and a few other minor changes, the method as a whole, together with its instructive text has been left intact, although I do not always agree with many of Baermann's statements. As to the musical contents it would be a sacrilege to change a note, as in my estimation there has been no other who has ever written so interestingly and effectively for the Clarinet as did Carl Baermann.

—Gustave Langenus.

CHAPTER I.

(a)   Historical Notes.

The invention of the Clarinet is credited to a flute maker named Johann Christoph Denner, who was born in Leipsic, 1655, and who died in Nuremberg in 1707. Its very first manufacture is said to have taken place between 1690 and 1708, naturally in a very unsatisfactory manner, as compared with the perfected instruments of modern times. These first specimens of the Clarinet were constructed with seven holes and two keys,

for the A   and Bb

All the other semi-tones had to be produced artificially by relaxing the lips and withdrawing the mouthpiece. The difficulties of producing a chromatic scale evenly and in tune under such conditions will be apparent to every clarinet player.

The necessity for improvement was therefore soon felt, as the Clarinet, even in this, its primitive form, gave promise of remarkable future usefulness.

The most prominent instrument makers of those times were Barthold Fritz, credited with adding the C sharp – F sharp key; Joseph Beer, the A flat – E flat key; Xavier Lefevre, the C sharp – G sharp key; Stadler, Kriesling, Schott and Ivan Muller, who after incessant experiments and trials, finally succeeded in producing a thirteen keyed Clarinet. This instrument was in good tune throughout and its smoothness of tone and technical possibilities surpassed all previous Clarinets.

However, Muller's contemporaries considered this "new" system too complicated and in spite of considerable financial assistance, Muller was finally compelled to wind up his business and leave Paris.

In 1839, L.A. Buffet, the famous French instrument maker, exhibited a Clarinet in Paris to which he had applied the mechanical system which Theobald Bohm had applied to the Piccolo and Flute, but the patent for this instrument was not granted until 1844. Buffet and Klose are equally credited with having brought the so-called Boehm system Clarinet to its present state of efficiency and no greater progress in Clarinet manufacture seems possible than has been achieved in the production of the modern seventeen keyed, six ring Boehm system Clarinet; this instrument undoubtedly possesses all the most desirable qualifications of tone and tune and its technical possibilities are more than ample while music remains in its present stage of development.

Upon this instrument the chromatic scale can be rendered perfectly pure and its execution has become a matter of comparative ease.

However, unremitting diligence is required for the mastery of any instrument, and particularly one which calls for double exertion and endurance, since in its service, it employs one of man's noblest organs – the lungs.

(b)   Different Parts of the Clarinet.

"As a rule, the clarinet consists of five pieces; the mouthpiece, barrel, upper and lower joints and bell. (See Figure I.)

Mouthpieces are made of the hardest material obtainable, such as ebonite and crystal, in order to give the maximum stability to the lay, which through atmospheric changes is liable to warp.

The barrel joint is convenient for tuning purposes. It can be secured in different lengths to order.

The upper and lower joints are detachable for the sake of conveniently carrying the instrument in a case.

The bell is chiefly ornamental; a continuous straight tube of the right length to emit the E and B would do as well.

mouthpiece

barrel

upper joint

lower joint

bell

Figure I

(c)   The Lay.

The lay is that part of the mouthpiece upon which the reed lies. It must be perfectly level, except near the tip, where the two sides slope away from the reed, leaving a small opening for the reed to vibrate upon. This opening varies in different facings.

(d)   The Reed and Ligature.

The reed is a thin piece of cane cut from a certain tall grass, Arundos Sativa, grown on the Mediterranean Coast. It plays an important part in tone production and great care must be exercised in its selection. The reed must not be so hard as to cause effort in playing. Ease and naturalness are the desiderata to be held in view; these are only to be obtained with a good mouthpiece and a good reed. The ligature secures the reed to the lay. The reed is placed centrally and the point must not overlap the tip of the mouthpiece."

CHAPTER II.

How to Hold the Instrument.

Since aesthetics should form the foundation of art in its every detail, it is most important for the pupil from the very beginning to acquire a graceful manner of holding the instrument, as well as a natural, unaffected posture of the body. The upper part of the body should be kept as straight and erect as possible, in order that the chest may be thrown forward and the taking of breath be properly and easily managed. The feet should be placed about a foot and a half apart. The instrument itself should be held gracefully and naturally, the left arm which manipulates the left-hand joint, being about a hand and a half's breadth distant from the body. Special care must be taken to hold the forefinger in such a way that, when lying in position, above the hole, it may open the A and A-flat keys with merely a slight movement. The thumb of the left hand must also be held in such a manner as to be able to manipulate the B and B-flat keys with ease and through a mere curving of the first joint. This is most important, as otherwise it would be impossible to bring about a smooth connection between the lower and the upper register, since the B and B-flat keys, beginning with the tone B

give life and color to all ascending tones. The right arm, which holds the lower piece, stands farther forward, since, from the point at which it is taken in the mouth, the instrument itself recedes more and more obliquely from the body, so that at the place where the thumb of the right hand takes hold of the holder, it should be about three hands distant from the body. The fingers should rest lightly and without stiffness upon their several holes and keys, and a finger when raised, must not move from its place.

The greatest obstacle to be met with in the course of correct technical development is a certain faulty habit of drawing the fingers in and raising them back again. This produces a cramped feeling in the hand, besides removing the fingers too far from the respective places in which they should remain.

It is hardly necessary to say that much depends on the build of the pupil's hand, and that longer fingers require different placing than shorter ones. This is a point which must be left to the teacher, who will doubtlessly choose the right method, without departing too much from the principles, laid down in the above chapter.

CHAPTER III

Embouchure.

Embouchure is of the greatest importance for tone production, and it may best be described as tone-production itself.

There is a class of clarinetists that play with the reed turned up, although I cannot ascribe any good reason for such a method of tone-production.

Whoever considers the structure of the mouth must become convinced without delay that this method is a wrong one for the following reasons: The stronger or weaker pressure of the lip on the reed is of the utmost importance for the production of tone; every

degree of pressure acts so decisively on tonal color and articulation that the finished artist will ultimately experience that every tone, properly speaking, has its own embouchure, though this of course, is an enigma to beginners.

Now, then, how is it possible to master all these finer shadings with the upper part of the head and its lips, since that part is utterly motionless! Motion is possible only for the lower jaw of the human head, and it is on that account that the reed should be turned down, to be managed by the lower lip. Moreover, the stroke of the tongue (staccato) is of great importance. It is impossible to give the three varieties of staccato – the sharp, the soft and the tied – with proper distinctness, if the tongue, instead of encountering the reed, infringes on the rigid mass of the inverted upper part of the mouthpiece. Therefore, I say, "Down with the reed to the underlip." Some players, too, take the mouthpiece so far into the mouth as to cause anxiety lest they choke themselves with the instrument. To say nothing of such an extremely unaesthetic spectacle, the method in itself is poorly suited for tone-production; with it, the tone will be somewhat hollow and pinched, and lack the noble quality which makes it resemble the human voice.

Many Clarinetists play with the upper and lower lip drawn over the teeth, which may have some advantages, as the tone appears to the player himself – though in reality it is not – to be smoother, a point to which I shall refer by and by. But in view of the endurance required in our time, in orchestra, as well as in concert-playing, the new method – that of placing the teeth directly on the upper part – has come to be acknowledged as the most expedient, and it is this method which I have adopted in the present school. Those players who think that with this position the tone loses in smoothness, are greatly mistaken. The direct application of the teeth to the mouthpiece causes the "player himself" to be deceived at first, for the following reason: The two hard objects – tooth and wood or plate of silver – induce a vibration in the interior of the human head, which is communicated to the ear of the player; the outsider and listener, however, cannot perceive any difference whether the upper lip is drawn over the teeth or not.
This deception, moreover, occurs only at first and gradually disappears entirely.

It is easily conceivable that anyone accustomed to playing with the lip drawn over the teeth, should upon giving up this method, find his tone changed; this change, however, is caused rather by the novelty and uncertainty of the embouchure, than through employment of the new method itself. Let the player continue for a fortnight with the new embouchure, and he will soon find his former experience reversed. All my pupils, and among them very able artists, have gladly adopted this method, and find it more natural and efficient than the former one, as thereby the endurance, and as necessary consequence, the certainty is at least doubled.

As to the lipping or embouchure itself, the teeth must be set about half an inch from the point of the mouthpiece. The under lip must be drawn lightly over the lower teeth and find its place of itself, directed by the adjustment of the teeth; the corners of the mouth must be firmly closed, so that the air rushing into the instrument may find no other escape.

The cheeks must likewise be drawn in as much as possible and should not, on any account, be inflated; for this is both ungraceful and prejudicial to the production fo a good tone. The higher the tones ascend, the more imperatively do they require a firm and delicate treatment by means of the upper lip. The reed should be pressed more and more strongly against the face of the mouthpiece, so that the air-space between the two may be contracted, because the high notes require less wind and the vibrations of the reed become shorter. Just the contrary, of course, takes place when the tones descend to a lower pitch, so that, on reaching the lowest tone, the under lip must be greatly relaxed, in order that the reed may vibrate without hindrance. An inviolable law for the beginner is "to lip with deliberation and repose"; practice, with time and patience, will enable him to find the proper embouchure for a given tone, without his having to hunt for it through all possible variations.

CHAPTER IV
The Trill (Rules)

In its correct technical treatment, the trill is one of the most difficult embellishments, and requires diligent and perservering study. Undeniably, the trill, like technic tone-formation, the staccato, and in general all that pertains to higher art, presupposes natural gifts on the part of the player. I have known virtuosi, who, with the most finished technic, could not produce a beautiful trill, and others again who could not produce a staccato with certainty, no matter how hard they would practice. However, a method of instruction cannot take account of individual talent or lack of same, but must call for greatest diligence to satisfy the requirements of art; even he whom nature has not gifted with special talent, will by diligent striving after perfection, achieve, at least so much as to be able to cover up his imperfections artistically and with discretion.

The trill consists of two tones following in rapid and frequent alternation; according to the key-signatures of the piece, these will form either a major or a minor second, the lower of the two tones being the principal tone, upon which the trill, properly speaking, is made. Whether the second formed by the trill is major or minor, depends, as we have just said, upon the key-signature; hence it would be a gross musical blunder to play a trill upon this note:

with E-Sharp and upon this:

with E-flat, unless one or the other, in spite of the signature, were especially intended, which would have to be indicated by placing a natural (♮) over or beside the trill-sign for the first case, a flat (♭) for

the second, or in other cases a sharp (♯).

There are various kinds of trills, though, on the whole, they do not differ very essentially from each other. Thus, with some the trill is begun with the higher note; for example:

with others, of whom I am one, with the note upon which the trill stands, thus:

My reasons for preferring the latter method are: firstly, the tone, upon which the trill is produced, is given out more decidedly thereby; and secondly, there is an unplesant feeling connected with the downward trill of the first method.

As a rule the trill closes with a turn, consisting of the tone one degree below the principal tone, immediately followed by the principal tone; but these two tones must follow each other just as quickly as those of the trill.

Together with the turn, attention must be paid to the signature of the piece and to the key in which the principal tone of the trill is, so as to decide correctly, whether the turn be played with a semitone or a tone below. The careful composer generally indicates his intention with small notes following the principal note of the trill, for instance:

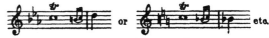

In *sostenuto* passages, or in very slow movements as *adagio, largo, larghetto,* the turn should be broader and slower than the trill itself, and even the trill should often be commenced more slowly: the latter in particular, when, as is frequently the case, the principal tone of the trill is preceded by its appoggiatura or mordent, written in full; for example:

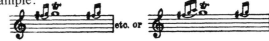

The best judge in such cases must be the player's own refined and artistic taste.

When the trill-sign (〰) is placed over or under the note, it indicates the trill without a turn; however, I use this but very infrequently as this kind of trill does not form a good close. I use it only in a series of trills quickly following each other (chain-trills), for instance:

When the trill is preceded by an appoggiatura consisting of the note below the principal tone, and this principal tone itself, as:

or, of three notes, the first of which is one degree below the principal tone itself, and the third one degree above the principal tone, as:

it is called a trill from below.

The exact reverse is the trill from above, as shown herewith:

These trills are usually given in full with their appoggiaturas indicated, as above.

Another kind of trill is the *Mordent,* also called half-trill. Its duration depends upon circumstances and upon the character of the passages. The older masters, such as Clementi, etc., teach that it should be made downward, but in modern times it is subjected to the law of the trill, being made with the ascending *Second* (major or minor), with and without a turn. Its sign is ⏦. The following passages

would be played as follows:

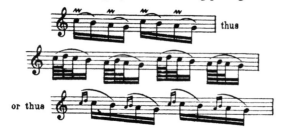

Whether such a succession of trills should be played quickly or slowly, depends chiefly upon the tempo of the piece. The old masters employed so great a variety of trills and turns that we could not possibly enumerate them all. In fact, this is hardly necessary for a clarinet-school, inasmuch as the modern notation either gives them plainly written in full or indicates, with exactness, their suitable appoggiaturas and turns. Furthermore, the effect will be quite identical, whether I play the following passage:

The difference is either hardly discernible, or of little consequence.

CHAPTER V

EMBELLISHMENTS.
The Appoggiatura and the Turn.

Like the trill, the *appoggiatura* and the *turn* are classed as belonging to the so-called embellishments in music. As I shall not attempt to include a general treatise on the theory of music in this method, I will introduce only such examples of the above-mentioned embellishments as concern practical and essential needs of the Clarinet player. As to the *appoggiatura,* ir will suffice to say that it is either long or short, and can from any possible interval with its principal tone; however, if short, it should always be in harmonic relation to that tone. The long appogiatura is generally marked by a note of greater value than the short appoggiatura. For instance:

In this case too the *appoggiatura* requires a stronger accent than the principal tone. Before a whole, half, quarter, eighth, etc., it has half the value of the note itself, which then has only the value of the note; before a tied note, as for instance:

it has the full value of the principal tone, which latter has only that of the note tied to it; such, at least, is the doctrine of the old school. I do not, however, agree with it in all cases, for the above example is certainly more beautiful and correct, when played thus:

Many of the old masters have written many of the so-called "passing-notes" as appoggiaturas. Here is an illustration from Cherubini's opera "The Water Carrier."

which every one would play:

Appoggiaturas of this kind are found in abundance in the works of Mozart, Handel, Gluck, Haydn, etc.

The short *appoggiatura,* as its name implies, is played exactly in the opposite manner, and, being short, the accent falls upon the subsequent note. For the sake of greater precision, this brevity of execution is indicated in modern notation by a a little line through the tail of the note:

As this indication is not contained in the music of the old masters (except in modern revisions), taste, experience and above all, correct understanding of the passages to be interpreted, must decide whether the appoggiatura be long or short.

The *turn* is also a most effective embellishment. If used with discretion and played with skill it will add much to the artistic taste of a performance. In former times it was used to excess, but this has been remedied entirely by our modern school of composers.

The *turn* consists of four notes, the note above the written or principal note, the written note itself, the note below, and again the written note. The sign is a turn  generally placed after the principal note. In this way a measure such as the following:

is played this way:

When the note is dotted, the last tone of the turn, which is again the principal tone, must receive the value of the dot. To illustrate:

is played as follows:

Dotted notes of less value, such as the following:

are played in this fashion:

An accidental (♯ or ♭) below the sign applies to the lower tone, and above it, to the upper tone. If supplied with an accidental both above and below:

it is played like this:

It is a difficult matter to lay down positive rules as to when the lower tone of the *turn* should be a halt or whole tone below, as in some cases the one is as correct as the other. However, one rule may be given: the *turn* on the *Tonic,* and also on the Fifth of the scale, requires the half-tone below the prinicipal tone; moreover, it may be said in general, that, when the upper tone of the *turn* is a whole-tone above the principal tone, the lower one is a half-tone and vice versa. However, the upper tone of the *turn* must always be in conformity with the natural scale in which it occurs. Therefore, to play the following,

In this way would be wrong

The correct way to play it would be:

In former times, the signs for the turn were frequently used for many embellishments which are now written out plainly in notes. Too many signs

N5724

cause confusion, and modern composers prefer writing:

CHAPTER VI.
The Signs of Expression.

Rich as music is in its inner life and as the language of the soul, just so poor is it in appropriate signs adapted to indicate everything the composer might wish to express. Of course, we have many indications for the tempo, from the slowest *largo* to *prestissimo,* but nevertheless, there are infinite varieties of tempi possible between these two extremes, which can never be indicated in plain words. It might be claimed that with the metronome we cannot go astray! True, the metronome prevents serious errors of tempo in general; nevertheless, it frequently occurs that in certain passages the steady beat of the Metronome is intolerable, and that a *ritardando, rallentando, accelerando* or *stringendo* indicate the proper movement only in a most imperfect manner. In cases like these, the refined taste and feeling of the player must point out the true way, and indicate, whether to accelerate or to retard. On the other hand, in *ensemble-playing,* the individual must adapt his playing to the performance as a whole, and this in turn to the conductor. The signs of dynamic expression are also most imperfect, and merely give approximate indications.

The following are the expressions for indicating the tempo, from the slowest to the very quickest; *Adagio; Grave; Largo; Larghetto; Lento Andantino; Andante; Allegretto; Moderato; Tempo giusto; Maestoso; Comodo; Allegro; Vivace; Con Spirito; Spiritoso; Con Brio; Con Fuoco; Furioso; Presto; Prestissimo.*

By way of modification, other words are prefixed to these, such as: *Molto; di molto*(much)*; assai* (very); *non troppo* (not too much); *un poco* (a little); *quasi* (almost, it were); *piu* (more); *meno* (less); *piu tosto* (rather); *sempre* (always); *ma* (but); *con* (with); *senza* (without); *con moto* (with motion); *brillante* (brilliant); *agitato* (excited, excitedly); *scherzando* (playfully); *sostenuto* (sustained); *a tempo* (in strict time); *ad libitum* (at pleasure); *rallentando* or *ritardando* (slackening the speed); *accelerando* and stringendo (increasing the speed); etc., etc.

Marks of *dynamic* expression are as follows: p. for *piano* (soft); pp. for *pianissimo* (very soft); *dolce* (sweet); *mezzo,* or (half); f. for *forte*(loud); ff. for *fortissimo* (very loud); *con tutta forza* (with the whole strength); fz. or sfz. for *forzando* or *sforzando* (strong accentuation of a tone); *crescendo* or the sign ＜(increasing in power); *descrescendo, morendo, diminuendo,* or the sign ＞(decreasing in power); *cantabile* (singing); *affectuoso* (tenderly); *grazioso*(gracefully, elegantly); *con espressione* (with expression); *con grand' espressione* (with great expression); . *con dolore* (grievously); *con energia* (with decision, energy); *tenuto* (abbreviated *ten.*); indicated in this school by a little line above the note (–) indicates that the note is to be sustained for its full value. In accordance the practical dynamic signs at our disposal may be grouped as follows: *p.; pp.; f.; ff.; fz.; sfz.;* or $>$ *ten.* or; *cresc.* $<$*; descresc.* $>$.

Properly speaking, there are but three kinds of articulation, viz. *slurred, detached* and *mixed.*

A *slur* or *curve* $\frown$ over the notes indicates that the notes covered by the curve must all be slurred, i.e., smoothly connected *(legato.)* Notes with *dots . . . .* or *accents* "" over or under them, must be detached and cut short by a stroke of the tongue *(staccato).* If some notes are slurred and others detached it results in mixed articulation, for instance:

Slurred or *legato* articulation may also be varied, if some of the notes are grouped as follows:

There are two kinds of detached articulation *(Staccato),* the *hard* and the *soft.* The former must be produced by the tongue; very sharp and short on the reed of the mouthpiece, in the same way as if one were to pronounce *tee, tee, tee,* very sharply. *Dots or accents* over or under the notes are the signs for this style of staccato, for instance:

The soft slurred staccato must be produced in a delicate manner, with the tongue, and should sound as though the player were to pronounce, *dee, dee, dee, dee, dee,* very softly and smoothly. Dots within a slur indicate this style of staccato:

In addition to these, there are various modifications of the staccato, but the pupil should confine himself to the usual forms, as indicated by the above-explained signs.

CHAPTER VII.

Interpretation.

Feeling for beauty is mysteriously implanted in the human soul, and one of its manifestations is seen in the wonderful effects, which music produces upon the heart. Yet, by reason of the mysterious nature of music, it is impossible to formulate absolute and specific rules for producing such effects, and we must content ourselves with laying down certain general principles of musical interpretation, for the guidance of reproductive artists.

The principal rules of interpretation for the pupil are the following: he should take special care to render everything *exactly as written,* observing all signs, and explaining to himself all the possible *reasons* for them; above all, he should beware of *false phrasing,* not playing a passage like this:

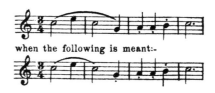

when the following is meant:-

Furthermore, he should not commit the common fault of playing dotted notes without reference to their strict value, for instance:

Moreover, he should play all unaccented parts of the bar broadly, if they do not consist of short notes, and keep a watchful eye on the accented parts (especially on the first beat of a bar), and not hurry over the last notes of a bar, when they form the introduction to the following one. Above all things he should also accustom himself to observe the prescribed tempo, in order to play exactly in time, for freer playing is only in place for advanced instrumentalists.

Again we observe that of two slurred notes the first one is to be sustained for its full value, and that as a general rule, ascending tones imply increased emotion and vice versa. However, there are many exceptions to this general rule; as often as possible the pupil should try to hear good players of the instrument, and if he himself be gifted with talent and feeling, he will learn more from such listening than he ever could from books. With regard to the compositions of the great masters, it is the duty of the reproductive artist to study them in regard to the individuality of their writers, and to play them in accordance with each one's characteristics. To play Mozart like Beethoven, or Weber like Spohr, would betray a lamentable lack of musical understanding. On the other hand, there are innumerable other compositions intended for the display of virtuosity, which the player may perform and interpret according to his own individuality and taste. In such pieces the delivery is so free that one and the same composition sounds almost like two different ones, when differently conceived and rendered. Who has not heard a piece performed by two artists, each with a different interpretation, without being able to decide, which was the more correct, since each performance produced the effect of a sudden inspiration of the artist himself! Now, this is the highest phase of artistic reproduction. However, it does not imply that the player may change the fundamental character of a piece at will, but only that in expressing joy, grief, rest, etc., etc., each one may follow his own feelings, and thus imbue the piece performed with his own individuality. Art has its rules and laws, but no fetters. Lastly, it is to be observed, that the reproductive artist must have a clear understanding himself, of what he intends to express, and how he will do it. He must have made the piece entirely his own, as it were, must remain true to its character, both in conception and rendition, and be able to illustrate both, with the most refined taste and elegance. Therefore, the reproductive artist should possess at least enough musical education to enable him to read a piece from score, in all its harmonic and melodic significance. Without this knowledge he may, perhaps, rank as a gifted amateur, but he will never merit the name of musician and artist, in the strict sense of those words.

CHAPTER VIII.

Explanatory Remarks on Breathing.

Breath is to a wind instrument player, what the bow is to a violinist. It follows that its proper management and manipulation is of the greatest importance.

The first rule as to this point is that the breathing should be regulated according to the length of the passage to be played; the player should take so much breath as to enable him to continue with ease till the next breathing place comes; under no circumstances must he try to continue playing until his breath fails entirely; this would exhaust him so completely that it would be impossible for him to blow the subsequent passage with sufficient steadiness.

The question as to when breath should be taken, may be answered very definitely. Music consists of periods, and these again of many phrases; at the end of such a phrase breath should be taken afresh. In this work the taking of breath is indicated by the sign as in the following example, in which that sign marks the end of a phrase corresponding with the slurs.

Again: breath may always be taken after a tied, or a longer dotted note: for example:

and before any tone on the unaccented part of the bar:

moreover, in quick runs, after the highest or lowest note aimed at by the run, or after the first note of the bar, or just before the last note, as in the following examples:

Between the last note of a bar and the first of the next one, breath may be taken only when the musical phrase ends on the last note of the bar, and and a new phrase, or the repetition of the former one, begins with the new bar. Of course the phrases spoken of here, cannot begin on an unaccented part of the bar, as this would involve an evident contradiction. In the following example the places for taking breath are correctly indicated:

the meaning of the musical phrase is completely changed. In consequence it will be most apparent how important it is to take breath properly, and how much it contributes to the clearness and intelligibility of refined and musical interpretation. Therefore, in all rules for taking breath, the following point must be strictly remembered, viz:—that the musical phrase must be kept intact, and that, whenever it is absolutely necessary to interrupt a phrase by taking breath, it should be as rarely as possible at the beginning of a phrase.

On no condition, should breath ever be taken immediately after a leading tone or immediately before a trial note. Therefore, taking a breath as indicated in the following example would be utterly wrong and unmusical:

I repeat the advice, to be very careful about taking breath between two bars, as nothing appears so bungling as a mutilated phrase and an irregular manner of breathing.

As already mentioned, I have indicated the places for taking breath in the course of this method, most accurately by the sign, ∾ for the special guidance of the pupil. I might add, that for the sake of greater expressive freedom, more frequent breathing may be indulged in, especially in passages requiring impulsive or intense feeling, special examples of which will be found in this school.

CHAPTER IX

Technic.
The purpose of technical study is to enable the player to master the important needs of his instrument, such as beauty and purity of tone and facility of execution in every detail.

While this study must be pursued under different conditions on different instruments, the essentials of a thoroughly developed technique are substantially the same on all instruments, and the purity and beauty of tone-production, as well as the independence of the fingers, must be developed so completely that the player will be enabled to cope with every possible requirement he might chance to meet.

There is scarcely another instrument which requires so much care and attention in regard to tone-production as does the Clarinet; with incompetent playing, its tone can become positively vulgar, while in the hands of an accomplished artist, the human voice can be imitated with astonishing perfection. However, the highest degree of finger-dexterity is of no avail without beauty of tone, as tone is the means through which the artist speaks to the hearts of men, the fingers merely serving as mechanical appliances for changing the pitch. The cultivation of technical proficiency on the other hand, must also receive its full share of attention, as without complete development of finger dexterity, no artist can ever hope to master the instrument in its every detail.

The majority of great composers of the past were also great virtuosi on some instrument and there can be no doubt that this circumstance had great influence on their works. The foundations of technic, as of everything else, must be laid with care and diligence; the weaker and less tractable fingers must be exercised in such a manner as to strengthen them and render them obedient to the will of the player. A number of exercises for this purpose are found in this work. We have already alluded to the influence of natural talent. But without serious study, even the most gifted will never succeed as they should, for only continuous and unwearied application has produced great players and great works. *True merit consists, not in genius or talent, but in diligence.* Therefore, the student should endeavor in every way to perfect his technic, regardless of criticism which may accuse him of developing his virtuosity for the sake of sensational ends alone. Undoubtedly, he who has no higher aim in attaining virtuosity, than to astonish the multitude or for monetary gains, hardly deserves to be classed among artists. But to him who unites a highly developed technic with musical understanding, to whom virtuosity is but a means, enabling him to give free rein to his genius and fancy, to him the highest prize will be awarded, in spite of criticism, owing to the delight and satisfaction he will always be able to arouse through means of his technical facility and artistic interpretative powers.

CHAPTER X

Additional Remarks as to the Necessary Requirements of Clarinet-playing;
Tone Production on the Reed.

Whoever intends devoting himself to playing the Clarinet should be positively certain that he possesses sufficient will-power and endurance for mastering this difficult instrument. The bodily requirements are; good health, a strong, sound chest, and good teeth (the *front teeth* at least must be in good condition.) The intellectual requirements are: geniality, appreciation of the beautiful in art, capability of enthusiasm, a delicate sense of tone and a good ear, impartial criticism and just valuation of one's own performances, acknowledgment and appreciation of the merits of other artists and a determination to persevere in perfecting one's art to the utmost of one's ability.

We have already spoken of the necessity of a *noble, beautiful tone.* The tone is beautiful, when it has a full, vibratory, metallic, clear sound, and retains its character in all ranges and shadings; when it does not lose its beauty, nor have a sharp, cutting effect in *fortissimo,* and is so susceptible to expression and modulation as to be applicable with ease to the most delicate passages, and will allow passing with perfect smoothness from one tone to another,—in a word, when it resembles a full, beautiful soprano voice. If *this register* (which is the finest on the Clarinet) is *beautiful,* the lower tones will also be necessarily good. But even if the tone possesses all these properties, yet lacks that peculiar property, "the soul," all else will be of no avail. As in the case of every other instrument played with a mouthpiece of cane, everything depends upon a good reed, and this is a most important point about a Clarinet. Without the good will and humor of this tyrant the greatest artist is but a tyro on his instrument, painfully, yet vainly striving to produce effects. In fact, the greater the artist, the more keenly he feels his dependence on the excellence of his reed.

In conclusion, I shall add a few remarks as to the preparation of a reed according to my own methods and as I have found same necessary for my own uses. In spite of all efforts to find a better material for the reed, we must always fall back upon that which was used from the very beginning, *cane,* the best quality of which, for our purposes at least, grows in the south of France, Africa and Italy. The cane varies in quality; sometimes it is softer, sometimes harder, sometimes of coarser, sometimes of finer fibre. In my opinion, a clarinet-reed is best: Firstly, after having been thoroughly dried for years, it has remained sound and not become too hard, (since to render it serviceable in such quality it would have to be made so thin, that the tone would be very piercing); secondly, when the pores are delicate and closed, when the weed, on cutting, shows a fine olive and golden yellow color, and when if striking the whole joint on some hard substance it will easily give out a clear tone. Such a joint is then to be taken and split lengthwise, somewhat wider than the face of the mouthpiece and cut to the required length of the reeds with a fine saw. Then, with a sharp knife, the inside hollow part of the wood is to be cut tolerably level. Herein particular care must be taken to cut in such a way, that the pores run straight, from one end of the piece to the other; this can be the case only with a piece which *grew straight,* and such pieces generally make the best reeds. Then the piece is to be reduced first by a coarse, then by a fine file, to about the required thickness. In order to obtain uniform thickness in all reeds, a flat piece of brass or German silver had best be taken, making an incision in it with a file about the proper thickness of the reed, and using this as a measure. If the reed has the approximate thickness, examine very carefully, if the filed side is, perfectly *level,* this is one of the *most essential* qualities of a good reed. By laying the reed on a piece of *thick* plate-glass the inequalities may easily be discovered. Such inequalities are best removed by grinding the reed fine and even on a piece of sandstone, somewhat more than a foot long and from five to six inches wide, which has been ground perfectly even. It is best to have several such stones and to grind them one upon another, so as to ensure a perfectly flat surface.

The reed, made perfectly even and smooth, is now wetted with the mouth and then allowed to dry; this is repeated till it remains quite fine. Then, by means of the files and afterwards of the sandstone, the piece of cane is made to take the shape of the reed, according to the lay of facing of the mouthpiece; for that purpose, it is laid upon a small piece of wood planed perfectly even, and somewhat wider, and perhaps again as long as the piece of cane, and is again moistened· so as to adhere better to the longer piece of wood; after this it should be held fast with the finger and cut down towards the point, so that the length of the cut of the reed is about a sixteenth of an inch less than that of the cut of the mouthpiece. Then, starting from the beginning of the cut, the reed should be made thinner and thinner towards the point and as evenly as possible on both sides; following this, the cut should be made to run down to the point *on as perfect a level* as can be, with a fine file, and the reed will then be finished in the rough. The reeds (of which I generally prepare six or twelve at a time) are now moistened once more, laid on a larger piece of plate-glass and kept there for eight or ten days in a moist state by wetting them with the mouth as soon as they get dry. This process effects a complete closing of the pores, and thereby facilitates the finishing of the reeds. After this I take the reeds from the glass, clean them thoroughly, polish them on the sandstone once more and examine by laying them on the smaller piece of plate-glass, as to whether the polished side has become warped. This warping, as a rule, may easily be remedied, but when it cannot be done, the reed ought to be thrown away.

Having made sure that the reed is *perfectly level,* it should be moistened and made to stick to a window-pane, with the light striking through it and any inequalities which may be visible should be rubbed down with a piece of Dutch rush (equisetum or horsetail) also moistened.

The reed should then be laid on the mouthpiece, to which it is tied by a string (I prefer this to a band with a screw) and dried. If it is still too stiff, it should be laid on the window again and rubbed down, till it blows more easily. Further rules on this point cannot be given, as everything depends on the greater hardness or softness, as well as on the degree of porosity of the piece of cane from which the reed is made.

I add some of my experiences; if the reed is too thick at the point, the tone will be hard, or, as clarinetists say, will not speak easily. If the lower register blows hard, the reed usually has an extraordinarily high compass, and has too much wood at the beginning of the cut. If the reed is too thin at the point, the tones are apt to whistle like a poor violin-string; if too much wood is cut away at the beginning of the cut, the *lower register* loses its beauty of tone. If the cane is *soft,* the reed should be *kept thicker throughout* and the reverse, if the cane is *hard.* Should the player find it impossible to sustain the *piano,* the reed should be thinned out, if it is strong enough, *towards the point;* sometimes, too, it is well to try one's luck below the *middle* of the reed. It is also to be observed, that, when a new reed has been played for a day or two, it should be polished off again on the back, as the pores will have become visible again.

However, the obstinacy of this little piece of wood often bids defiance to all precautions, and I hereby wish all my colleagues the best of luck and a reed which will last for a life-time.

—CARL BAERMANN.

Before the student can commence to play any Instrument it is necessary that he should be acquainted with the rudiments of musical Notation.

The signs, which indicate pitch and duration of a musical sound, are called Notes figured thus:  etc.

They are named after seven letters of the alphabet; C. D. E. F. G. A. B. and are written on, between, above or below five parallel lines, ≡≡≡ called the Stave, the names of which are determined by Clefs, placed on different lines.

For this instrument, only the treble or G clef is used, which is placed on the second line.

The names of the notes on the five lines are:

E G B D F

of the four spaces between the lines: F A C E of the two above and below the lines D G

These eleven notes are insufficient to indicate the full compass of Sounds in use.

Ledger lines have therefore to be added, above and below the stave in order to signify higher and deeper sounds.

Notes of the ledger lines above the stave

A B C D E F G A

Notes of the ledger lines below the stave

C B A G

FULL TABLE OF ABOVE NOTES.

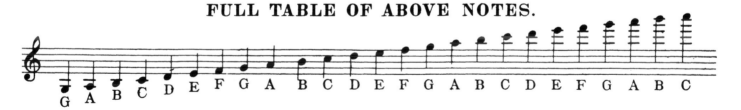

G A B C D E F G A B C D E F G A B C D E F G A B C

DURATION OF NOTES.

Notes may be of longer or shorter Duration which is shown by the peculiar form of each note.

Forms of different notes.

Whole note; *Half note;* *Quarter note;* *Eighth note;* *Sixteenth note;* *Thirtysecond note.*

Several of the latter three specimens combined may also be written thus:

Eighth notes; *Sixteenth notes;* *Thirtysecond notes.*

COMPARATIVE TABLE OF THE RELATIVE VALUE OF NOTES.

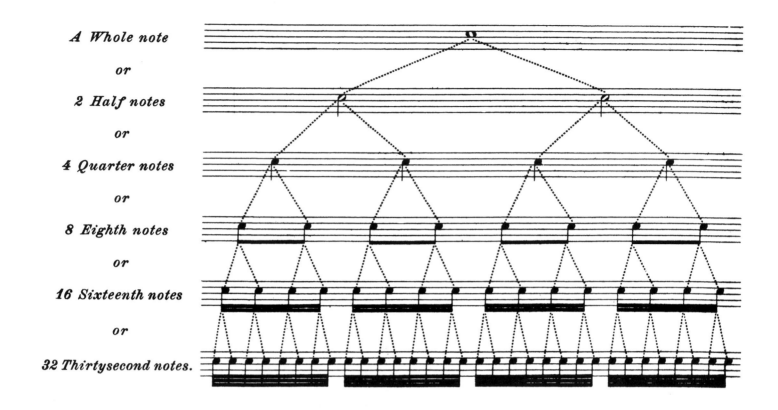

A Whole note

or

2 Half notes

or

4 Quarter notes

or

8 Eighth notes

or

16 Sixteenth notes

or

32 Thirtysecond notes.

BARS.

Notes are systematically arranged into <u>bars</u>, marked by one or two lines drawn across the stave.

One line ≡ is placed after each bar and each bar contains the same number or value of notes, and each bar must last precisely the same length of time. The end of a part of a composition is marked with two lines or a double bar, and if either two or four dots are found by the side of the double bar thus: ‖: the whole part from the preceding double bar, or if there is no earlier double bar then from the beginning of the piece is to be played again. This is called a <u>Repeat</u>.

RESTS.

Instead of a Note a <u>Rest</u> of equal value can be placed.

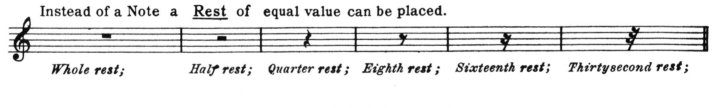

Whole rest;   *Half rest;*   *Quarter rest;*   *Eighth rest;*   *Sixteenth rest;*   *Thirtysecond rest;*

DOTS.

A <u>Dot</u> placed after any note or rest increases its value one half, thus:

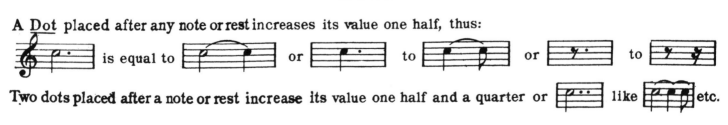

Two dots placed after a note or rest increase its value one half and a quarter or likeetc.

TRIPLETS, DOUBLE TRIPLETS AND GROUP.

Triplets are marked by a *3* being put over a group of three notes. Double Triplets are marked by a *6* being put over a group of six notes. Three quarter notes marked thus ![thus] must be played in the same time as two quarter notes ![two quarter] not so marked; or six eighth notes ![six eighth] in the time of four eighth notes ![four eighth] not so marked. There are also groups of five ![five] seven ![seven] and nine notes ![nine] etc.

TIME.

In order to know how many quarter notes, eighth notes or sixteenth notes a bar contains, special figures are placed at the beginning of a movement.

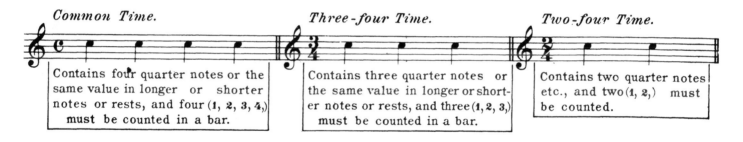

Common Time.	*Three-four Time.*	*Two-four Time.*
Contains four quarter notes or the same value in longer or shorter notes or rests, and four (1, 2, 3, 4,) must be counted in a bar.	Contains three quarter notes or the same value in longer or shorter notes or rests, and three (1, 2, 3,) must be counted in a bar.	Contains two quarter notes etc., and two (1, 2,) must be counted.

TABLE OF TIMES.

Single Common Times.   *Compound Common Times.*   *Single Triple Times.*   *Compound Triple Times.*

When a line is drawn through the **C** thus: **¢**, which is called àlla breve. two is counted in a bar.

SCALES.

The ladder-like succession of eight sounds, starting from any note and ascending or descending by tones and semitones in regular order, is called a *Scale,* and each note of a scale is called a *Degree.*

Between these eight degrees there are seven intervals or distances, five of which are tones, and two semitones.

There are two principal kinds of Scales, termed *Major* and *Minor,* whose ascension or descension is diatonical: i.e. in tones and semitones, and a third kind, whose ascension or descension is chromatic: i. e. only in semitones.

For the present, only the *Major* scale will be discussed.   In the *Major* scale the semitones are situated between the third and fourth and the seventh and eighth degrees of the scale.

EXAMPLE.

Each diatonic scale derives its name from the name of the note on the first degree— or the *root.*

There are twelve major and twelve minor scales; but not to burden the student with their combination at present, only the scale of C major will be given.

The distance from one note to another is called an *Interval.* Two notes placed on the same degree do not produce any interval, they are said to be in *Unison.*

The intervals are named: the Second, the Third, the Fourth, the Fifth, the Sixth, the Seventh, the Octave, etc.

EXAMPLE.

Degrees:
1   2   3   4   5   6   7   8

Intervals: Second,   Third,   Fourth,   Fifth,   Sixth,   Seventh,   Octave.

SHARPS.

A Scale may be formed on any note, but in order to produce semitones between the third and ourth and seventh and eighth degrees in any other but the scale of C major, it is required to employ certain characters, which raise degrees, or restore the pitch of any note in the scale.

One of these characters is called a sharp(♯), which, when prefixed to a note raises it a half tone.

The number of sharps employed in a scale depends upon which note, the scale is founded.

The sharps succeed each other in the following order:

Thus it will be seen that if one sharp is employed it must be prefixed to F, consequently all F's in that piece must be raised half a tone. When two sharps are employed all F's and C's must be raised, and when three sharps are employed all F's, C's and G's must be raised and so on.

Table of Signatures of Sharp Keys.

FLATS.

A flat (♭) prefixed to a note lowers it half a tone.   The flats succeed each other in the following order:

The same rule concerning signatures as with sharps is to be observed here.

Table of Signatures of Flat Keys.

THE MINOR SCALES.

Every major scale has its relative minor, the root of which is to be found on the sixth degree of the major scale. Both scales bear the same signature. There are two kinds of *minor* scales, the *harmonic* and the *melodic* form.

THE MELODIC MINOR SCALE.

The ascending of the melodic *minor* scale differs from the descending, the former having its sixth and seventh degree raised by *accidentals not essential to the key*. In the ascending, semitones are situated between the second and third and the seventh and eighth degrees, and in the descending between the sixth and fifth and the third and second degrees.

SCALE OF A MINOR.
Without Signature; Relative to C major.

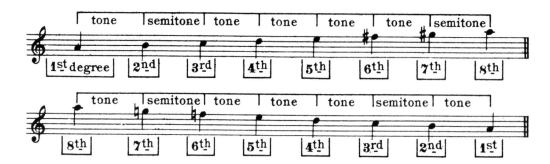

TABLE OF MINOR KEYS WITH THEIR RELATION TO MAJOR.

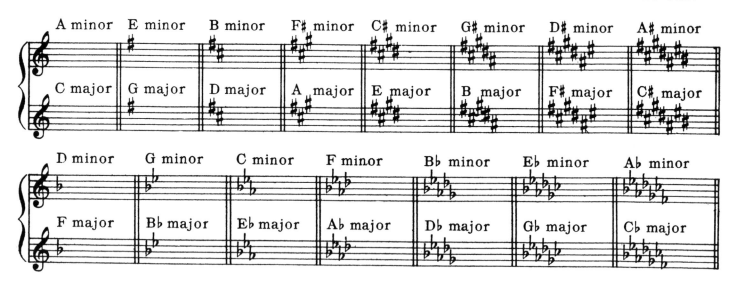

THE HARMONIC MINOR SCALE.

The Harmonic Minor Scale differs from the Melodic, as only its **7**th degree is raised by an accidental, which remains, whether ascending or descending.

SCALE OF A MINOR.

THE NATURAL ♮.

In order to restore a note which has been raised by a sharp ♯ or lowered by a flat ♭, a *Natural* ♮ is employed which restores it to its natural pitch.

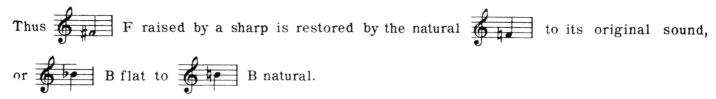

Thus [staff] F raised by a sharp is restored by the natural [staff] to its original sound, or [staff] B flat to [staff] B natural.

THE DOUBLE SHARP ×.

By prefixing a double sharp × to a note the same must be raised a whole tone.

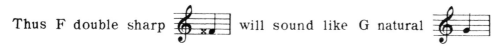

Thus F double sharp [staff] will sound like G natural [staff]

THE DOUBLE FLAT ♭♭.

A double flat ♭♭ prefixed to a note depresses the note a whole tone. Thus [staff] B♭♭ (double flat) will sound like A natural [staff]

THE PAUSE ⌒.

A Pause ⌒ placed over a note, means that the note can be sustained to an indefinite length at the performer's pleasure; the counting being interrupted.

THE CHROMATIC SCALE.

Consists of a succession of semitones, which, in ascending are designated by sharps, and in descending by flats.

Abbreviations are employed in written music to avoid repetitions of a single note or passage.

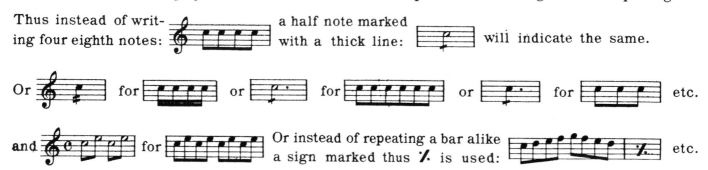

Thus instead of writing four eighth notes: a half note marked with a thick line: will indicate the same.

Or for or for or for etc.

and for Or instead of repeating a bar alike a sign marked thus ⁒ is used: etc.

TRANSPOSITION OF THE KEYS.

When C is taken as **1**, the scale or key is said to be in its natural position; but either of the other letters may be taken as **1**, in which case the scale is said to be *transposed*. As **1** is the basis of the scale, the foundation on which it rests, so the letter which is taken for this sound is called the *Key-note*. Thus, if the scale be in its natural position, it is said to be in the key of C; if G be taken as **1**, the scale is in the key of G; if D be taken as **1**, the scale is in the key of D; and so on with the rest of the seven letters; which ever letter is taken as **1**, that letter becomes the key-note of the scale.

In transposing the scale, the order of the intervals or tones and semitones, must be preserved. Thus, the interval must always be a *tone* from **1** to **2**, a *tone* from **2** to **3**, a *semitone* from **3** to **4**, a *tone* from **4** to **5**, a *tone* from **5** to **6**, a *tone* from **6** to **7** and a *semitone* from **7** to **8**. The interval from one letter to another letter is also the same and cannot be changed,—thus it is always a *tone* from C to D, and from D to E, a *semitone* from E to F, a *tone* from F to G, from G to A, from A to B, and a *semitone* from B to C. In the transposition of the scale therefore it becomes necessary to introduce sharps and flats, or to substitute sharped or flatted letters for the natural letters, so as to preserve the proper order of the intervals.

First transposition by sharps from C to G, a fifth higher, or a fourth lower.

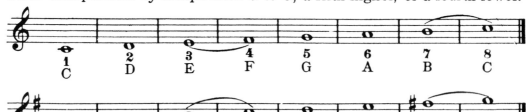

The same method is followed in the transpositions by sharps, viz: the fifth above or the fourth below is taken as **1** of a new key in every succeeding transposition and an additional sharp will be required in every succeeding transposition.

To transpose the scale by flats, we take the fourth (instead of the fifth) of every new scale. F is the fourth of C; hence it is **1** of the new scale (key of F.) The order of intervals must be the same in the flat key as in the sharp; hence the B must be made flat.

Transposition by Flats from C to F, a fourth higher or a fifth lower.

DIFFERENT SHADES OF TONE.

p   means: *piano,* soft.

pp   means: *pianissimo,* very soft.

f   means: *forte,* loud.

ff   means: *fortissimo,* very loud.

mf   means: *mezzoforte,* moderately loud.

cresc. or ⎯◁ means *crescendo,* increasing the sound.

dim. decresc. or ▷⎯ means *diminuendo, decrescendo,* diminishing the sound.

sf, rf or > means *sforzando, rinforzando,* sharply accentuated.

fp   means: *forte-piano,* loud and immediately soft again.

GRACES, EMBELLISHMENTS OR ORNAMENTS OF MELODY.

THE APPOGGIATURA.

The appoggiatura is a grace note placed above or below a principal note. When it is placed above, it is always at the interval of either a tone or a semitone. When it is placed below the principal note it should always be at the interval of a semitone. When the appoggiatura is written so  the value of it is one half of the following note.

When crossed by a small line, thus: its value is but one fourth of the note that follows it.

EXAMPLES.

Written thus:

Played thus:

There is also a double appoggiatura which is composed of two grace notes placed: the first, one degree below the principal note, and the second, one degree above.

Written thus:

EXAMPLE.

Played thus:

THE GRUPPETTO OR TURN.

Is composed of three grace notes placed between or after a principal note. The turn is marked thus: ∾. A small sharp placed under some of the signs thus: indicates that the lowest of the three grace notes is sharpened. Should the sharp be placed above the sign thus , the upper grace note must be sharpened; or in case of a sharp above and below the sign , the upper and lower grace note must be sharpened. The same rule applies to flats, only that the grace notes must be lowered half a tone in that case.

EXAMPLES.

With sharps and flats.

THE PASSING SHAKE.

The passing shake, often written thus ᷍, must be played quick and round in the following manner:

THE SHAKE.

The shake or trillo, marked thus *tr* consists in the alternate repetition of the note marked, with the note in the next degree above it.

EXAMPLE.

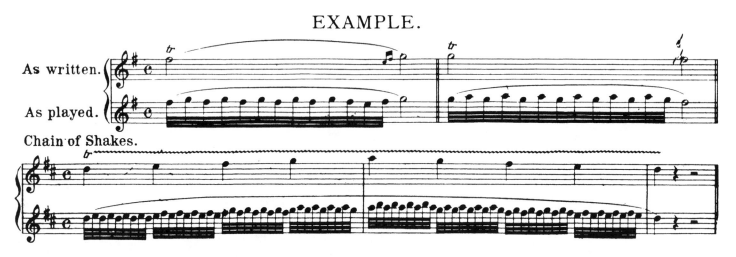

Chain of Shakes.

List of the Principal Words used in Modern Music
With their Abbreviations and Explanations

A	to, in or at; *a tempo*, in time
Accelerando (accel.)	Gradually increasing the speed
Accent	Emphasis on certain parts of the measure
Adagio	Slowly leisurely
Ad libitum (ad lib.)	At pleasure; not in strict time
A due (a 2)	To be played by both instruments
Agitato	Restless, with agitation
Al or Alla	In the style of
Alla Marcia	In the style of a March
Allegretto	Diminutive of allegro; moderately fast, lively; faster than *andante;* slower than *allegro*
Allegro	Lively; brisk, rapid
Allegro assai	Very rapidly
Amoroso	Affectionately
Andante	In moderately slow time
Andantino	Diminutive of *andante;* strictly *slower* than andante, but often used in the reverse sense
Anima, con } Animato	With animation
A piacere	At pleasure; equivalent to *ad libitum*
Appassionato	Impassioned
Arpeggio	A broken chord
Assai	Very; *Allegro assai,* very rapidly
A tempo	In the original tempo
Attacca	Attack or begin what follows without pausing
Barcarolle	A Venetian boatman's song
Bis	Twice, repeat the passage
Bravura	Brilliant; bold; spirited
Brillante	Showy, sparkling, brilliant
Brio, con	With much spirit
Cadenza	An elaborate, florid passage introduced as an embellishment
Cantabile	In a singing style
Canzonetta	A short song or air
Capriccio a	At pleasure, ad libitum
Cavatina	An air, shorter and simpler than the aria, and in one division, without Da Capo
Chord	The harmony of three or more tones of different pitch produced simultaneously
Coda	A supplement at the end of a composition
Col or con	With
Crescendo (cresc.)	Swelling; increasing in loudness
Da or dal	From
Da Capo (D. C.)	From the beginning
Dal Segno (D. S.)	From the sign
Decrescendo (decresc.)	Decreasing in strength
Diminuendo (dim.)	Gradually softer
Divisi	Divided, each part to be played by a separate instrument
Dolce (dol.)	Softly; sweetly
Dolcissimo	Very sweetly and softly
Dominant	The fifth tone in the major or minor scale
Duet or Duo	A composition for two performers
E	And
Elegante	Elegant, graceful
Energico	With energy, vigorously
Enharmonic	Alike in pitch but different in notation
Espressivo	With expression
Finale	The concluding movement
Fine	The end
Forte (f)	Loud
Forte-piano (fp)	Accent strongly, diminishing instantly to piano
Fortissimo (ff)	Very loud
Forzando (fz >)	Indicates that a note or chord is to be strongly accented
Forza	Force of tone
Fuoco, con	With fire; with spirit
Giocoso	Joyously; playfully
Giusto	Exact; in strict time
Grandioso	Grand; pompous; majestic
Grave	Very slow and solemn
Grazioso	Gracefully
Harmony	In general, a combination of tones, or chords, producing music
Key note	The first degree of the scale, the tonic
Largamente	Very broad in style
Larghetto	Slow, but not so slow as Largo; nearly like Andantino
Largo	Broad and slow; the slowest tempo-mark
Legato	Smoothly, the reverse of staccato
Ledger-line	A small added line above or below the staff
Lento	Slow, between Andante and Largo
L'istesso tempo	In the same time, (or tempo)
Loco	In place. Play as written, no longer, an octave higher or lower
Ma	But
Ma non troppo	Lively, but not too much so
Maestoso	Majestically; dignified
Maggiore	Major Key
Marcato	Marked
Meno	Less
Meno mosso	Less quickly
Mezzo	Half; moderately
Mezzo-piano (mp)	Moderately soft
Minore	Minor Key
Moderato	Moderately. *Allegro moderato,* moderately fast
Molto	Much; very
Morendo	Dying away
Mosso	Equivalent to rapid. *Piu mosso,* quicker.
Moto	Motion. *Con moto,* with animation
Non	Not
Notation	The art of representing musical sounds by means of written characters
Obbligata	An indispensable part
Opus (Op.)	A work.
Ossia	Or; or else. Generally indicating an easier method
Ottava (8va)	To be played an octave higher
Pause (⌢)	The sign indicating a pause or rest.
Perdendosi	Dying away gradually
Piacere, a	At pleasure
Pianissimo (pp)	Very softly
Piano (p)	Softly
Più	More
Più Allegro	More quickly
Più tosto	Quicker
Poco or un poco	A little
Poco a poco	Gradually, by degrees; little by little
Poco più mosso	A little faster
Poco meno	A little slower
Poco più	A little faster
Poi	Then; afterwards
Pomposo	Pompous; grand
Prestissimo	As quickly as possible
Presto	Very quick; faster than *Allegro*
Primo (Imo)	The first
Quartet	A piece of music for four performers.
Quasi	As if; in the style of
Quintet	A piece of music for five performers
Rallentando (rall.)	Gradually slower
Replica	Repetition. *Senza replica,* without repeats
Rinforzando	With special emphasis
Ritardando (rit.)	Gradually slower and slower
Risoluto	Resolutely; bold; energetic
Ritenuto	In slower time
Scherzando	Playfully; sportively
Secondo (2do)	The second singer, instrumentalist or part
Segue	Follow on in similar style
Simplice	Simply; unaffectedly
Senza	Without. *Senza sordino* without mute
Sforzando (sf)	Forcibly; with sudden emphasis
Simile or Simili	In like manner
Smorzando (smorz)	Diminishing in sound. Equivalent to *Morendo*
Solo	For one performer only. *Soli;* for all
Sordino	A mute. *Con sordino,* with the mute
Sostenuto	Sustained; prolonged
Sotto	Below; under. *Sotto voce,* in a subdued tone
Spirito	Spirit. *con Spirito* with spirit
Staccato	Detached; separate
Stentando	Dragging or retarding the tempo
Stretto or stretta	An increase of speed. *Più stretto* faster
Subdominant	The fourth tone in the diatonic scale
Syncopation	Change of accent from a strong beat to a weak one.
Tacet	"Is silent" Signified that an instrument or vocal part, so marked, is omitted during the movement or number in question.
Tempo	Movement; rate of speed.
Tempo primo	Return to the original tempo.
Tenuto (ten.)	Held for the full value.
Thema or Theme	The subject or melody.
Tonic	The key-note of any scale.
Tranquillo	Quietly.
Tremolando, Tremolo	A tremulous fluctuation of tone.
Trio	A piece of music for three performers.
Triplet	A group of three notes to be performed in the time of two of equal value in the regular rhythm.
Troppo	Too; too much. *Allegro, ma non troppo,* not too quickly.
Tutti	All; all the instruments.
Un	A, one, an.
Una corda	On one string.
Variatione	The transformation of a melody by means of harmonic, rhythmic and melodic changes and embellishments.
Veloce	Quick, rapid, swift.
Vibrato	A wavering tone-effect, which should be sparingly used.
Vivace	With vivacity; bright; spirited.
Vivo	Lively; spirited.
Volti Subito V. S.	Turn over quickly.

EXPLANATION OF THE SIGNS

To facilitate the connecting of any of these notes ♪♪♪ with any one of the following ♪♪♪ the right hand fingers should keep the holes covered. For instance, instead of raising the right hand fingers each time for the G in this passage ♪♪♪ they should remain on the holes. If the upper notes of this passage were C, C♯, or E♭, the little fingers could remain stationary on their respective keys. To denote when the fingers should remain on holes, the following signs are used *———△ and the above measure would be marked thus: ♪♪♪
♪ This sign indicates when to breathe.

ERKLÄRUNG DER BEZEICHNUNGEN

Um den Uebergang dieser Noten ♪♪♪ zu den folgenden ♪♪♪ zu erleichtern, sollten die Finger der rechten Hand die Löcher zuhalten, z. B. anstatt jedesmal die Finger der rechten Hand wegen der Note "G" aufzuheben, ♪♪♪ können sie auf den Löchern liegen bleiben. Sollten die oberen Noten einer Passage folgende sein: *C. Cis.* oder *Es,* dann könnten die kleinen Finger auf den in Betracht kommenden Klappen liegen bleiben. Um anzuzeigen, wann die Finger auf den Löchern liegen bleiben sollen, braucht man folgendes Zeichen *———△; oben angegebener Takt würde z. B. folgend bezeichnet: ♪♪♪
♪ Zeichen für Athem holen.

Method for the Clarinet
2d Division Preparatory Studies (Vorbereitungs Studien)

CARL BAERMANN, Op. 63
Edited by GUSTAVE LANGENUS

No 1 **Exercises for Fingering**
Griff Übungen

No 2 **Diatonic Studies with Accidentals**
Diatonische Studien mit Vorzeichnungen

19991-67

Nº 3

In Nº 3 the pupil must take special care that no intermediate tones be heard between the slurred notes. This fault is apt to creep in especially on taking hold of the B-B♭ key, which is taken with the left hand thumb, as for instance in the bars 7 and 8, 9 and 10. Breath must be taken afresh only at the sign (♪).

Bei dem Beispiel Nº 3 muss der Schüler sein vorzügliches Augenmerk darauf richten, dass zwischen den zusammen-gebundenen Noten keine Zwischentöne zu hören seien, welcher Fehler sich besonders gerne bei dem Ergreifen der H-B Klappe einschleicht, welche mit dem Daumen der linken Hand genommen wird, wie z. B. im 7. und 8., 9. und 10. Takte dieses Beispiels. Athem soll nur bei dem angegebenen (♪) frisch geholt werden.

Nº 4 C major *C dur*

Broken Chords *Gebrochene Accorde*

In the playing of all the scales each step must be intoned *piano* at the start, increase to *forte* and then gradually back to *piano* again. Each tone to be sustained as long as possible in order to strengthen the breathing and the embouchure. For a quicker rendition of the scales, study them, both legato and staccato. Broken chords are to be practised in two different ways as indicated above.

Bei allen Scalen muss der Ton piano angesetzt, bis zum forte gesteigert und wieder zum piano zurückgeführt werden. Der Ton überhaupt ist so lange als möglich auszuhalten, damit der Athem und der Ansatz gestärkt wird. Wenn die Scalen schneller gespielt werden, muss man dieselben gebunden (legato) und gestossen (staccato) studieren; die gebrochenen Accorde haben zweierlei Spielarten, was ebenfalls genau beobachtet werden muss.

Nº 5 Moderato

The following short technical exercises are very necessary and should be used for daily practice exactly as marked. Each measure to be repeated until the fingers are tired. This is all the more necessary as the exercises bring all the weaker fingers into use, strengthen them and make them more independent.

Folgende kleine eingestreute, aber höchst notwendige technische Übungen muss der Schüler täglich üben, und zwar folgendermassen: man wiederhole jeden einzelnen Takt so oft, bis die Finger ermüden. Es ist dies um so nötiger, weil diese Übungen die schwächeren Finger beschäftigen, dieselben stärken und selbständiger machen.

NB. As a matter of course the above exercises must be practised very slowly at first and gradually faster until they can be played fluently and without mistakes in quick tempo. This direction also applies to all the following exercises. At the same time, the sign ✱—△ indicating where the fingers are to remain on the keys, must not be overlooked, as it will facilitate matters considerably for the player.

In order that the embouchure of the pupil may not become too greatly fatigued, he should practise these exercises "silently" i. e., without actually producing the tones, part of the time, the more so as the exercises are intended more particularly for finger-practice. However, where the embouchure and fingering are of equal importance, as with the exercises for the higher tones, they should be practised as frequently "with tone" as "silently."

NB. Vorstehende Übungen müssen selbstverständlich anfangs sehr langsam geübt und so lange fortgesetzt werden, bis dieselben rein und ohne Anstoss im schnellen Tempo gehen, was auch bei allen nachfolgenden Übungen zu beobachten ist; ebenso darf das Zeichen ✱—△, welches das Fingerliegenlassen bezeichnet, nicht übersehen werden, da dies unendlich viel zur leichtern Spielart beiträgt.

Damit den Schüler der Ansatz *(Embouchure)* nicht zu sehr ermüdet, kann er auch diese Studien teilweise ohne zu blasen d. h. stumm üben, insoweit die Übungen sich blos mehr auf die Finger beziehen; sind aber Ansatz und Finger gleich wichtig, was bei den Übungen für die höheren Töne der Fall ist, so müssen diese wenigstens ebensooft laut, als stumm studiert wer~~

№ 7

Moderato

p legato

p

cresc.

f

p

№ 8

Allegro molto moderato

With rigid, hard stroke.
Hart gestossen.

mf

p

f

pp

mf

f

p

cresc.

sempre cresc.

f

№ 9

Moderato

With flexible tied stroke.
Gebunden gestossen.

p

p

p

This exercise to be played in Andante tempo at first, and gradually increasing in speed until it can be
№ 10 played Allegro, fluently and with ease.

Dieses Beispiel muss zuerst langsam und dann immer schneller studiert werden, bis es gut im schnellen Tempo geht.

№ 11 must be played in very strict time and with broad tone, so as to make it sound very imposing.
muss streng im Takt und mit breitem Ton gespielt werden, so dass dieses Stück sehr gewichtig lautet.

№ 12 must also, like № 10, be studied at first slowly, then quicker, up to Allegro.—Mixed staccato; play throughout with powerful voluminous tone.
muss ebenso wie № 10 zuerst langsam, dann immer schneller, bis zum tempo allegro studiert werden. Durchgehend gebunden und gestossen, mit Kraft und vollem Ton.

In exercise №12, the pupil must observe the slurs carefully, as they change continually. The sign for breathing has also been omitted, as it would require constant changing, the more rapidly the piece is played; it is specially to be remarked, that breath must be taken very quickly.

Bei dem Beispiel №12 muss der Schüler genau auf die Bindezeichen achthaben, da dieselben sich stets ändern, auch ist bei diesem Stück das Zeichen zum frischen Athemholen nicht angegeben, weil sich dasselbe, je schneller das Stück gespielt wird, immer verändern müsste; zu bemerken ist hauptsächlich, dass der Athem sehr schnell geschöpft wird.

№ 13

* 1.) Slur all the notes in each bar. 2.) Detach first note, slur second to third and detach fourth note.
3.) Slur first two notes and detach third and fourth.

1.) Sämmtliche Noten jedes Taktes sind gebundén zu spielen. 2.) Die erste Note im Takt ist gestossen, die zweite und dritte gebunden, die vierte wieder gestossen zu spielen. 3.) Erste und zweite Note sind gebunden, dritte und vierte gestossen zu spielen.

19991-67

№ 14

ROMANCE
ROMANZE

№ 15 In strict time and with full, broad tone.
in strengem Takt und mit vollem, breitem Ton.

No 17 **Continuation of short finger exercises.**
Weitere Folge von kleinen Fingerübungen.

№ 18 tranquilly
mit Ruhe

Molto moderato

In strict time
In strengem Takt

Allegro moderato

ELEGY
ELEGIE

№ 21 SYNCOPATIONS. SYNKOPEN.

Largo With fervor, and very slowly.   Mit tiefem Ernst und sehr langsam.

No 22 **With energy and power**
Mit Energie und Kraft

Allegro con moto

Allegro molto vivace; **quasi** presto

N.B. Beginning with №23, the sign (✱＿△) showing where and how long the fingers are to remai
upon the keys, will appear less frequently and when it does, more so as a reminder for the pupil, who, t
this time, is supposed to have become sufficiently acquainted with its meaning.

NB. Von №23 angefangen, wird das Zeichen (✱＿△) zum Fingerliegenlassen nur mehr sehr selten gesetzt werde
gleichsam nur zur Erinnerung für den Schuler, da er dessen Bedeutung aus den vorhergehenden Stücken genugsam ke
nen gelernt hat.

VARIATIONS
VARIATIONEN

NB. The sign (–) over or under a note indicates that the note should be somewhat sustained.

NB. Der kleine Strich (–) über oder unter der Note bedeutet, dass dieselbe etwas angehalten, d.h. breiter genommen wird.

12991-67

№ 26

D minor melodic   *D moll melodisch*

№ 27
Andante

* This study must be practised with exacting care; when played in rapid tempo (Allegro vivace) it is of great benefit even to advanced pupils.

* Diese Etude muss äusserst sorgfältig geübt werden; im schnellen Tempo (Allegro vivace) gespielt, ist sie selbst für weiter vorgeschrittene Schüler von grossem Nutzen.

19991-67

Nº 28 **Study for dotted notes.**
Etude für punktierte Noten.

Allegretto molto moderato

No 29 Continuation of short exercises.
Weitere Folge von kleinen Übungen.

52

19991-67

20 times
20 times

It is hardly necessary to say, that the pupil should not practise these little exercises all at once, but should ad‹ perhaps a new line every day to those already studied.   Such study, however dry and fatiguing, should be res‹ olutely carried through, in spite of everything, if the pupil seriously wishes to obtain a finished technic, with‹ out which nothing of any account can be accomplished.

Es braucht wohl kaum erwähnt zu werden, dass man diese kleinen Übungen nicht gleich über Hals und Kopf studiere, son‹ dern täglich vielleicht eine neue Zeile zu den früher gelernten hinzufügt. So troken und ermüdend dieses Studium auch sei mag, so lasse sich der Schüler durch nichts davon abhalten, da dies der wahre einzige Weg zu einer solid ausgebildeten Tech‹ nik ist, ohne welche kein grosses Ziel zu erreichen ist, da nur bei möglichst vollendeter Technik der Künstler sich ungehin‹ dert entfalten und seiner Fantasie folgen kann.   Ausdauer führt über die steilsten Berge,und der Erfolg belohnt jede Mühe

No 30 Bb major B dur

No 31
Andante molto cantabile

VAR.3 Brillante

60

N⁰ 33 G minor melodic *G moll melodisch*

N⁰ 34
Adagio

Agitato, quasi presto alla breve

№ 35

Allegro moderato alla Polacca

64

19991-67

No 36

LÄNDLER

№ 39

B minor melodic *H moll melodisch*

№ 40

Andante

p legato

ritenuto

A

f a tempo

p

cresc.

cresc. *p* *p* *cresc.* *p*

rall. B *p* *p* *ritard.* *pp*

l'istesso tempo

pp *p* *cresc.*

TARANTELLA

Allegro vivace quasi presto

No 42
Eb major *Es dur*

Nº 43 Adagio

Allegretto con moto

19991-67

Nº 45   A major *A dur*

Nº 46   Andante

No 47 Allegro grazioso

82

19991-67

Nº 48

C minor melodic – C moll melodisch

Nº 49

Adagio

A

P con dolore e con grand'espressione

fz

pp

cresc.

dim.

p

B

con espress.

cresc.

v

cresc.

p

pp

C

P con dolcezza

cresc.

f

p

dim.

p

cresc.

cresc.

f

p

dim.

pp

P con dolcezza

pp

morendo

№ 50

Allegro vivace

86

No 51 **Last series of short exercises.**
Letzte Folge von kleineren Übungen.

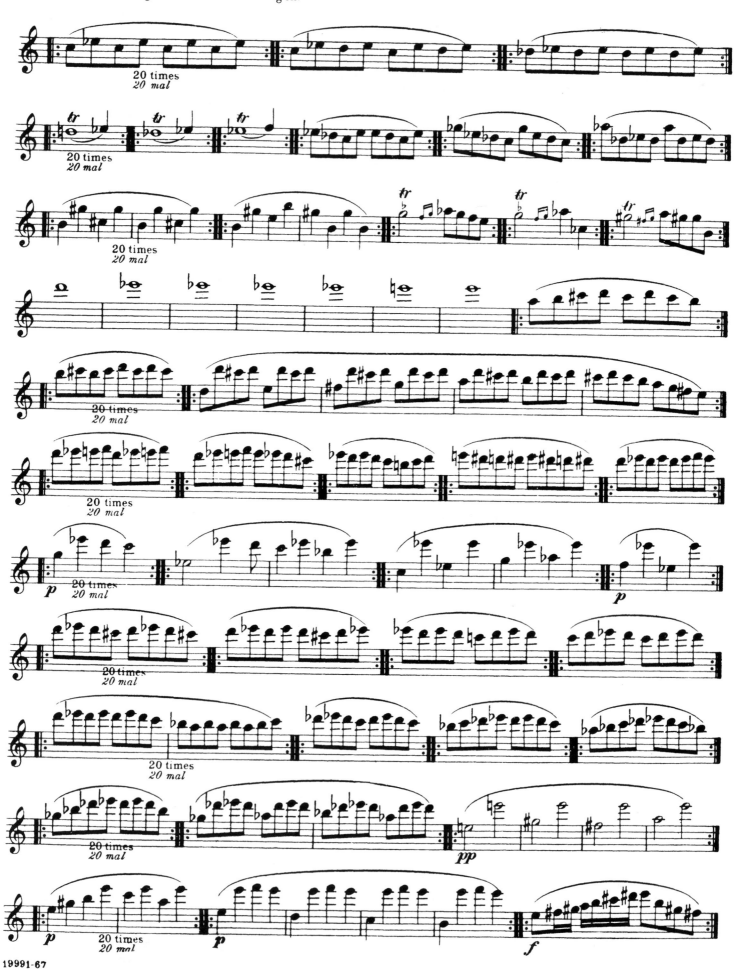

19991-67

Before conclusion of this Part II. all scales not included in the preceding pages will be taken up.
To take up pieces in these more difficult keys at this point would be premature and such material, as far
as it is practicable for the clarinet, will therefore be reserved for the fourth and fifth parts of this method.

Vor dem Ende des II. Teils folgen hier nur mehr die fehlenden Scalen.   Musikstücke in diesen schwierigen Tonarten
schon jetzt anzuführen wäre verfrüht, doch sind solche, soweit sie für die Clarinette ausführbar, im IV. und V. Teil enthalten.

№ 52

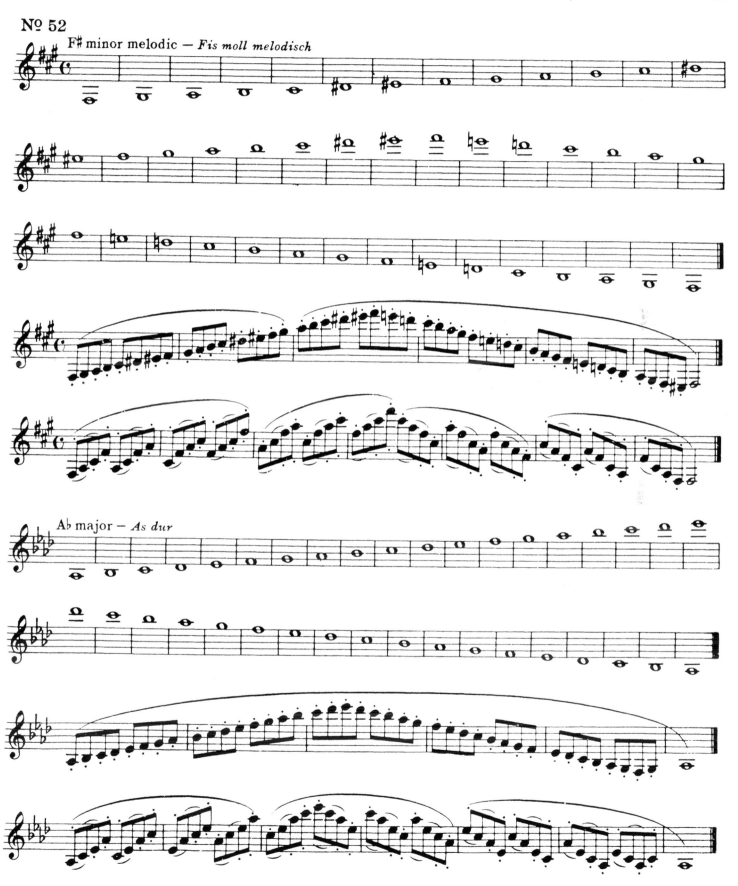

F# minor melodic — *Fis moll melodisch*

Ab major — *As dur*

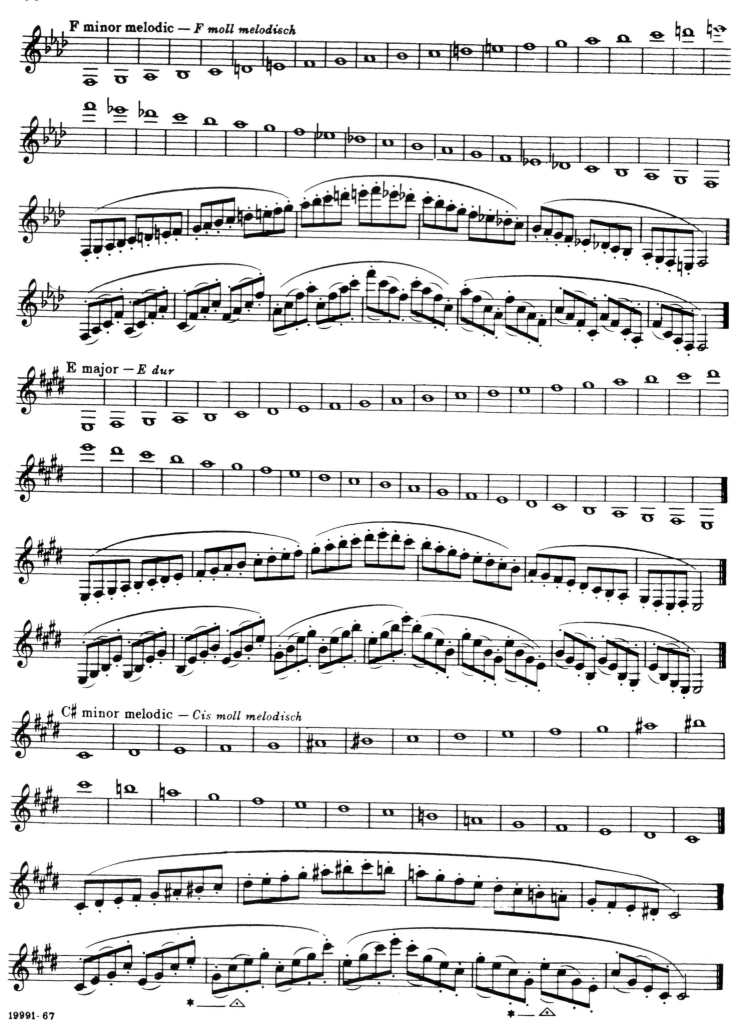

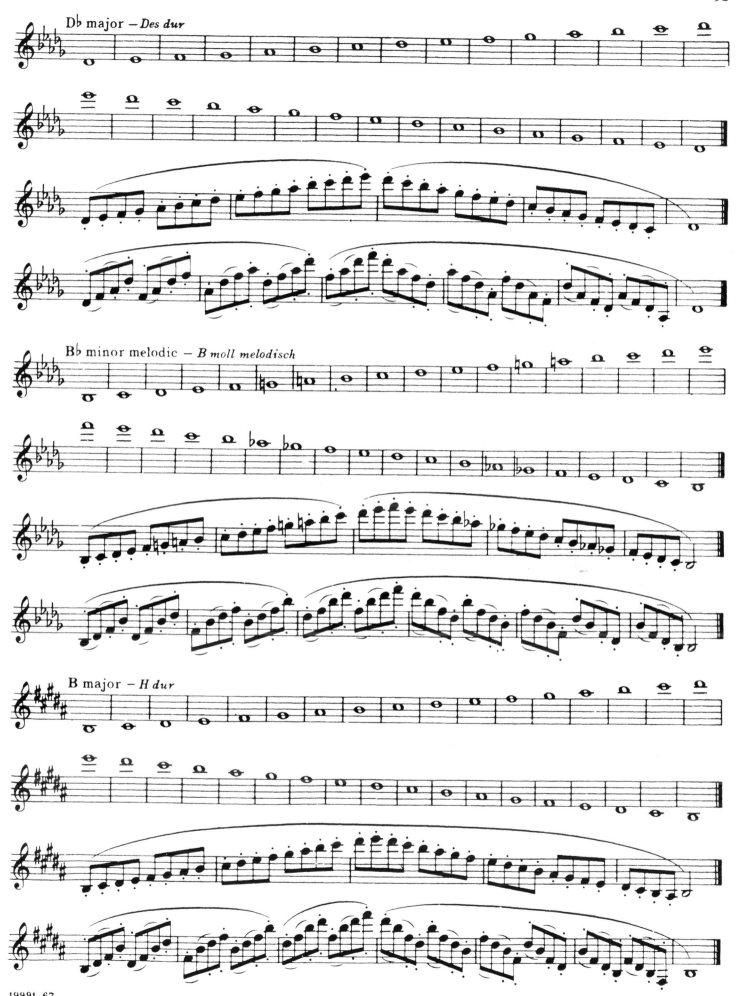

Db major — *Des dur*

Bb minor melodic — *B moll melodisch*

B major — *H dur*

92

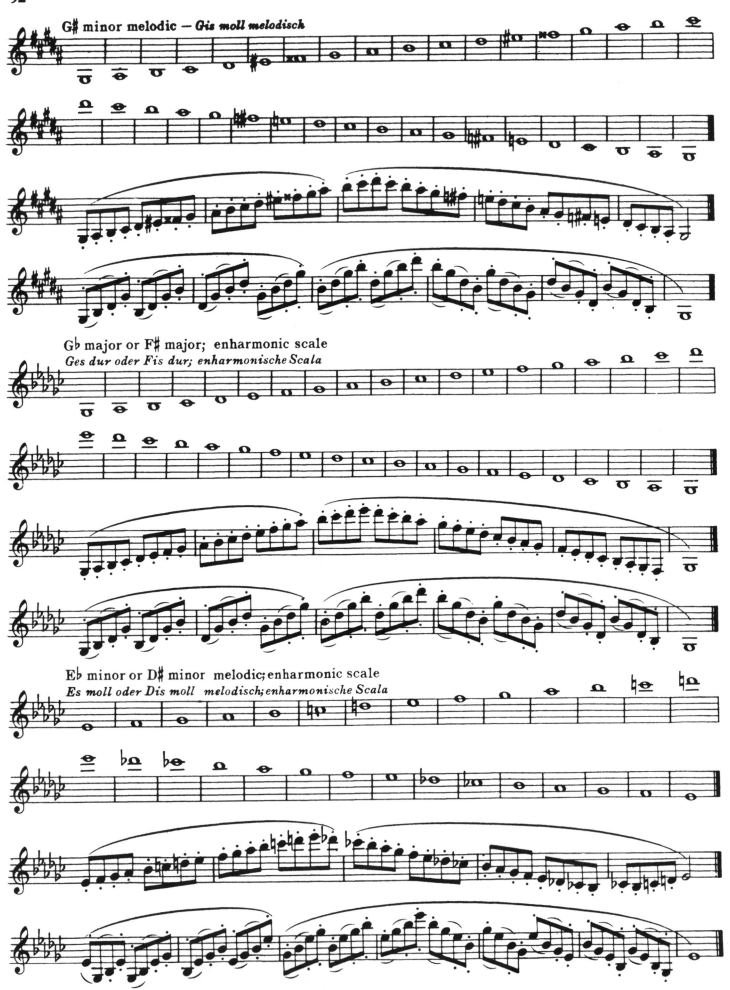

G♯ minor melodic — *Gis moll melodisch*

G♭ major or F♯ major; enharmonic scale
Ges dur oder Fis dur; enharmonische Scala

E♭ minor or D♯ minor melodic; enharmonic scale
Es moll oder Dis moll melodisch; enharmonische Scala

19991-67

PRACTICE PLANNER

Date	Page	Goals/Comments	Remarks
Date	Page	Goals/Comments	Remarks

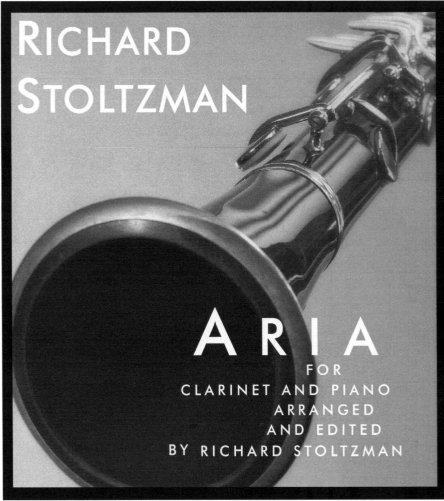
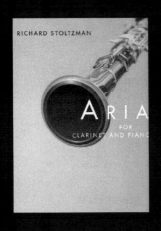

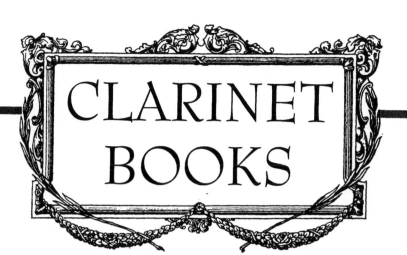

CLARINET BOOKS

Favorite Solos with Piano Accompaniments on CD

The Carl Fischer CD Solo Series is designed to help all levels of instrumental soloists improve their performances by making practice time more productive with the included "live" piano accompaniment.

The CD contains a beautifully recorded piano accompaniment performed by Melody Lord who has years of experience accompanying soloist of all ability levels.

The CD Solo Series is an invaluable teaching tool and is presented in 3 graded levels: Beginning (Gr. 2), Intermediate (Gr. 3) and Advanced (Gr. 4-5).

As an added bonus, the faster pieces in the Beginning Level have a second track with the piano accompaniment at a rehearsal tempo to assist in the preparation of the piece.

Works for Clarinet and Piano

In the Carl Fischer CD Solo Series

Beginning level

W2624	Arioso — Largo from *Concerto for Harpsichord and String Orchestra*	Johann Sebastian Bach
W2628	Gigue	Arcangelo Corelli
W2629	Gymnopédie No. 2 from *Trois Gymnopédies*	Erik Satie
W2630	Musical Moment from *6 Moments Musicaux*	Franz Schubert
W2579	Tambourin	François Joseph Gossec
W2627	Träumerei from *Scenes from Childhood* ("Kinderscenen")	Robert Schumann

Intermediate Level

W2582	Allegretto	Benjamin Godard, Op. 116, No. 1
W2584	Berceuse	Gabriel Fauré, Op. 16
W2583	Entr'acte from *Carmen*	Georges Bizet
W2581	Giga from *Sonata in F Major*	George Frideric Handel, Op. 1, No. 1
W2585	Sicilienne from *Pelléas et Mélisande*	Gabriel Fauré
W2625	Siciliano from *Sonata No. 2 in E♭ Major*	Johann Sebastian Bach
W2626	Sonata in F Major	Benedetto Marcello

Advanced Level

W2586	Concertino	Carl Maria von Weber, Op. 26
W2587	Concerto No. 1 in F minor for B♭ Clarinet and Piano	Carl Maria von Weber, Op. 73
W2588	Grand Duo Concertant	Carl Maria von Weber, Op. 120, No. 1
W2632	Introduction, Theme and Variations from *Sehnsuchts-Walzer* by Franz Schubert	Ferdinand David
W2590	Sonata in E♭ Major, Op. 120, No. 2	Johannes Brahms, Op. 120, No. 2
W2589	Sonata in F minor for Clarinet and Piano	Johannes Brahms, Op. 120, No. 1
W2631	Theme and Variations Fourth Movement from *Quintet for Clarinet and Strings*	Wolfgang Amadeus Mozart, K. 581